The Hare
and the
Tortoise

Retold by Sarah Keane

Illustrated by Anne Sulzer

HOUGHTON MIFFLIN COMPANY

BOSTON

ATLANTA   DALLAS   GENEVA, ILLINOIS   PALO ALTO   PRINCETON

One day, a hare and a tortoise
were having an argument.

The hare, who could run very fast, thought he was much smarter than the tortoise.

The tortoise could only move slowly and had to carry his house on his back.

3

"You are an old slow-poke,"
said the hare.
"You couldn't run if you tried."

4

The tortoise did not agree.

"I bet that I could beat you in

a race," he sniffed.

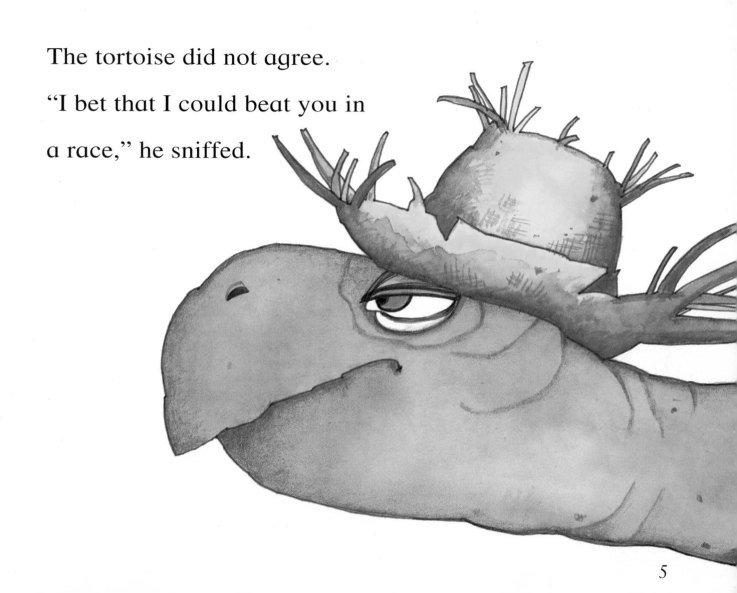

5

"Oh no you couldn't!" replied the hare.

"Oh yes I could!" said the tortoise.

"All right," said the hare, "let's have a race.

But I know I shall win, even if I run with my eyes shut."

They asked a passing fox to start them off.

"Ready, set, go!" said the fox.

The hare set off at a great pace.

The tortoise hardly moved.

In a few moments, the hare was so far ahead

that he decided to stop for a rest.

Soon he fell asleep.

After a while, the tortoise
came plodding along.

He passed the sleeping hare. Though he too was tired,

he didn't stop for a moment.

Suddenly the hare woke up.

He ran as fast as he could to the finish line, but he was too late.

The slow but steady tortoise had won the race.